PLEASE NOTE: THE AUTHORS & PUBLISHER RECOMMEND ADULT SUPERVISION ON ALL PROJECTS!

THE AUTHORS AND PUBLISHER OF HOWTOONS HAVE MADE EVERY REASONABLE EFFORT TO ENSURE PROJECTS AND ACTIVITIES CONTAINED IN THIS BOOK ARE SAFE WHEN CONDUCTED AS INSTRUCTED, BUT ASSUME NO RESPONSIBILITY FOR ANY INJURIES SUFFERED OR DAMAGES OR LOSSES INCURRED AS A RESULT OF FOLLOWING THE INSTRUCTIONS CONTAINED IN THIS BOOK.

DR. SAUL GRIFFITH
Co-creator, Writer & Engineer

NICK DRAGOTTA
Co-creator, Writer & Artist

INGRID DRAGOTTA
Project Design & Book Curator

JOOST BONSEN
Co-creator & Writer

OTHERLAB
Workshop & Laboratory

RICHARD STARKINGS & COMICRAFT'S JIMMY BETANCOURT
Letters
Intro & pages 2-9, 13-20, 22-27, 30, 73-88, 112-117, 137-157

LEE LOUGHRIDGE
Colors
Intro & pages 2-9, 13-20, 22-27, 30, 73-88, 112-117, 137-157

RUS WOOTON
Book Design

IMAGE COMICS, INC.
Robert Kirkman – Chief Operating Officer
Erik Larsen – Chief Financial Officer
Todd McFarlane – President
Marc Silvestri – Chief Executive Officer
Jim Valentino – Vice-President

Eric Stephenson – Publisher
Corey Murphy – Director of Sales
Jeremy Sullivan – Director of Digital Sales
Kat Salazar – Director of PR & Marketing
Emily Miller – Director of Operations
Branwyn Bigglestone – Senior Accounts Manager
Sarah Mello – Accounts Manager
Drew Gill – Art Director
Jonathan Chan – Production Manager
Meredith Wallace – Print Manager
Randy Okamura – Marketing Production Designer
David Brothers – Content Manager
Addison Duke – Production Artist
Vincent Kukua – Production Artist
Sasha Head – Production Artist
Tricia Ramos – Production Artist
Emilio Bautista – Sales Assistant
Jessica Ambriz – Administrative Assistant
IMAGECOMICS.COM

TROUBLE MAKERS

a HOWTOONS adventure.

MAKE'N TROUBLE

Intro to *making* and also some of the more *trouble* causing projects.

TOYS FROM TRASH

DROIDS

PLAY WITH YOUR FOOD

CONTENTS

ON A WONDERFUL LITTLE PLANET...

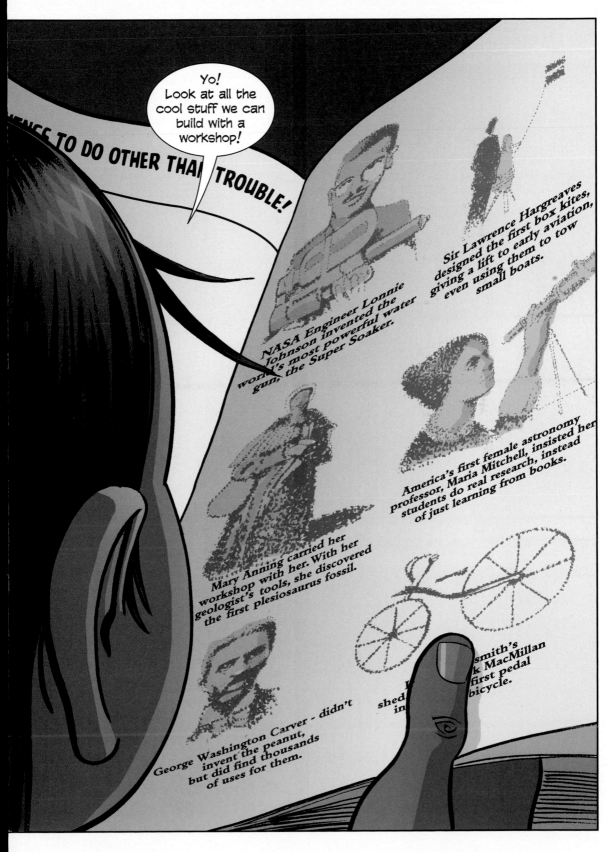

THERE ARE MANY, MANY, MANY PROJECTS TO UNDERTAKE...

...AND IN THE CRACKS OF THOSE PROJECTS AND BENEATH THE FILTHY UNDERBELLY OF YOUR LATEST FRUSTRATION IS SOMETHING SPECIAL...

...YOUR LATEST INVENTION!

WHOAH! BEFORE WE GET TO THE PROJECTILES, LET'S PROTECT OUR EYES.

WITH... **SODA BOTTLE GOGGLES**

CAN YOU FOLLOW THE WORDS AND PICTURES TO MAKE THESE GOGGLES?

RECYCLE 2-LITER BOTTLE

WASH OUT

FLATTEN

CUT OFF ENDS

CUT DOWN MIDDLE

DRAW ON FACE

DESIGN IT

CUT OUT

FOLD OVER SNIP SNIP

KNOT HEAD STRAP USE RUBBER BANDS

WARNING! THESE GOGGLES ARE TOYS AND **ARE NOT** TO BE SUBSTITUTED FOR **CERTIFIED SAFETY GLASSES** WHEN THEY ARE **RECOMMENDED!**

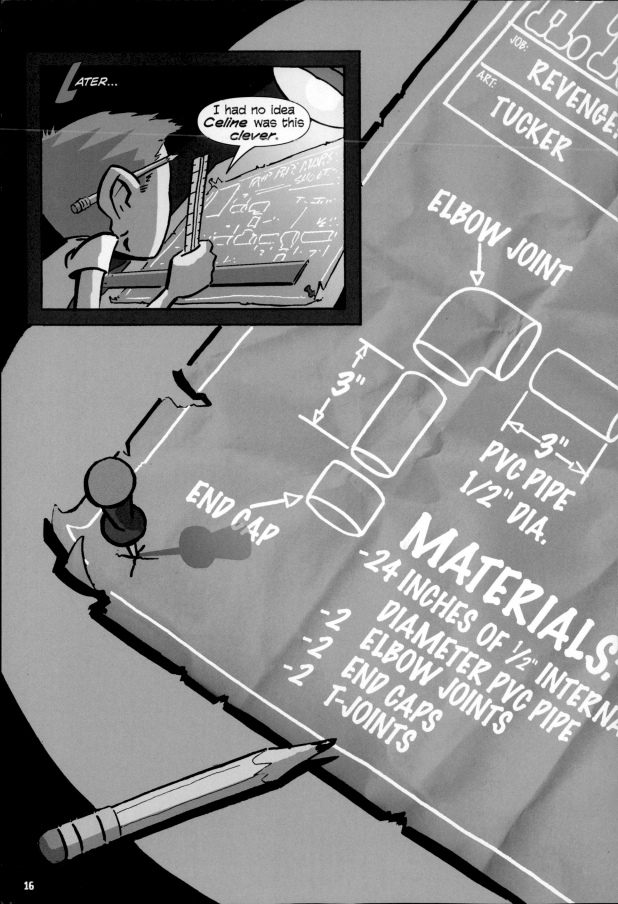

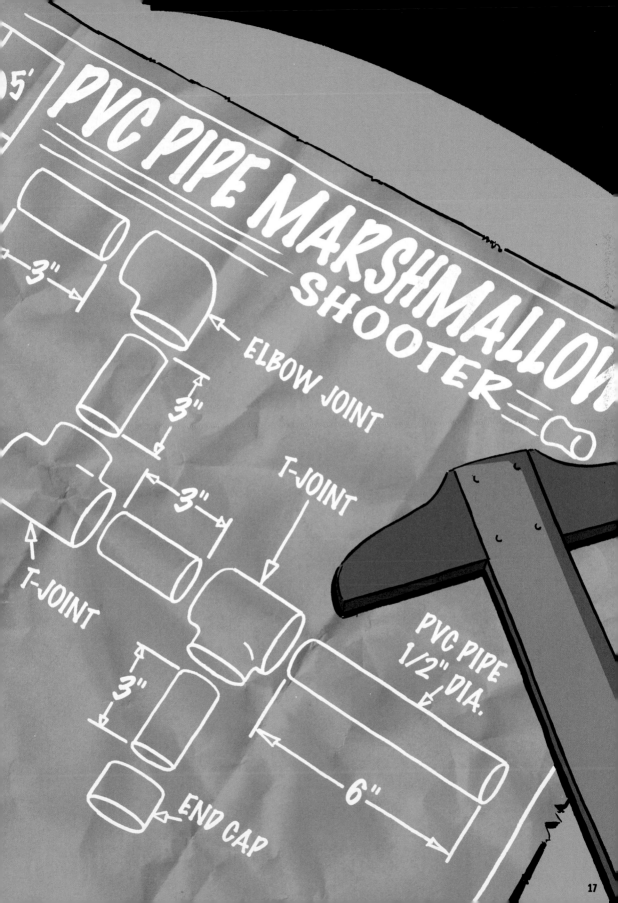

PVC PIPE MARSHMALLOW SHOOTER

5'

3"

3"

ELBOW JOINT

3"

T-JOINT

T-JOINT

3"

END CAP

PVC PIPE 1/2" DIA.

6"

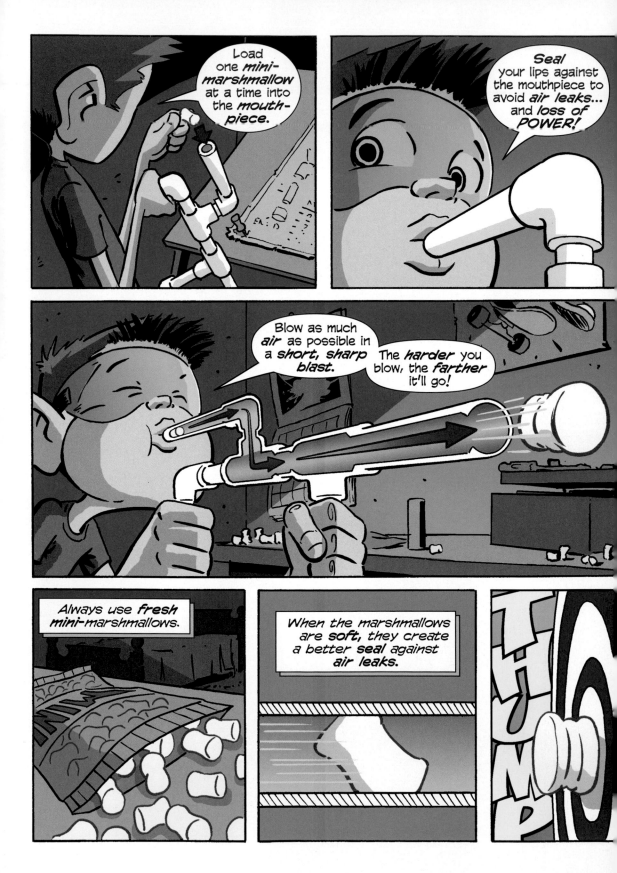

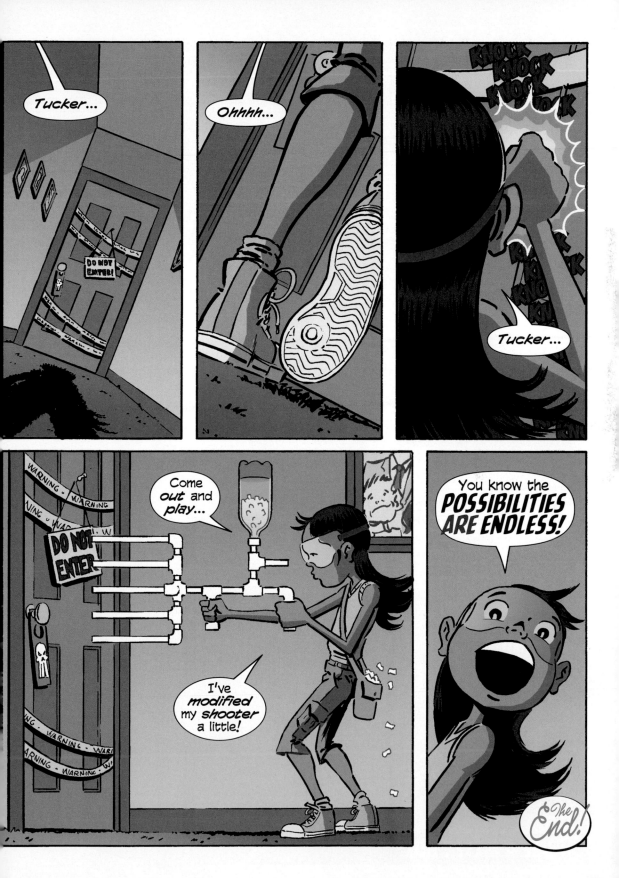

CUT TO THE POINT

YOU NEED A HACKSAW TO CUT THE PVC FOR YOUR MARSHMALLOW SHOOTER, AND IN FACT YOU WILL NEED SAWING SKILLS THROUGHOUT YOUR LIFE.

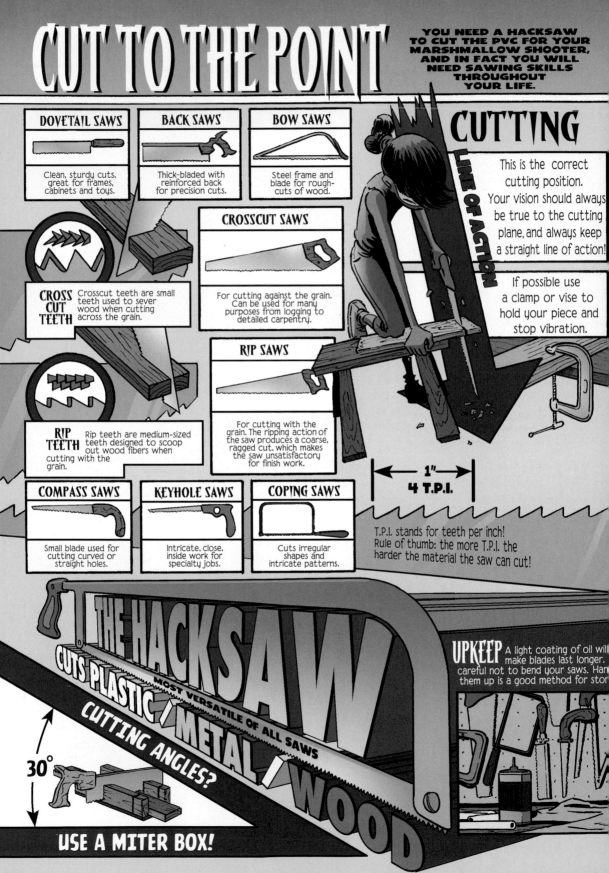

DOVETAIL SAWS
Clean, sturdy cuts, great for frames, cabinets and toys.

BACK SAWS
Thick-bladed with reinforced back for precision cuts.

BOW SAWS
Steel frame and blade for rough-cuts of wood.

CROSSCUT SAWS
For cutting against the grain. Can be used for many purposes from logging to detailed carpentry.

CROSS CUT TEETH Crosscut teeth are small teeth used to sever wood when cutting across the grain.

RIP SAWS
For cutting with the grain. The ripping action of the saw produces a coarse, ragged cut, which makes the saw unsatisfactory for finish work.

RIP TEETH Rip teeth are medium-sized teeth designed to scoop out wood fibers when cutting with the grain.

COMPASS SAWS
Small blade used for cutting curved or straight holes.

KEYHOLE SAWS
Intricate, close, inside work for specialty jobs.

COPING SAWS
Cuts irregular shapes and intricate patterns.

CUTTING

LINE OF ACTION

This is the correct cutting position. Your vision should always be true to the cutting plane, and always keep a straight line of action!

If possible use a clamp or vise to hold your piece and stop vibration.

1"
4 T.P.I.

T.P.I. stands for teeth per inch! Rule of thumb: the more T.P.I. the harder the material the saw can cut!

THE HACKSAW
MOST VERSATILE OF ALL SAWS

CUTS PLASTIC / METAL / WOOD

CUTTING ANGLES?
30°
USE A MITER BOX!

UPKEEP A light coating of oil will make blades last longer. Be careful not to bend your saws. Hang them up is a good method for stor[...]

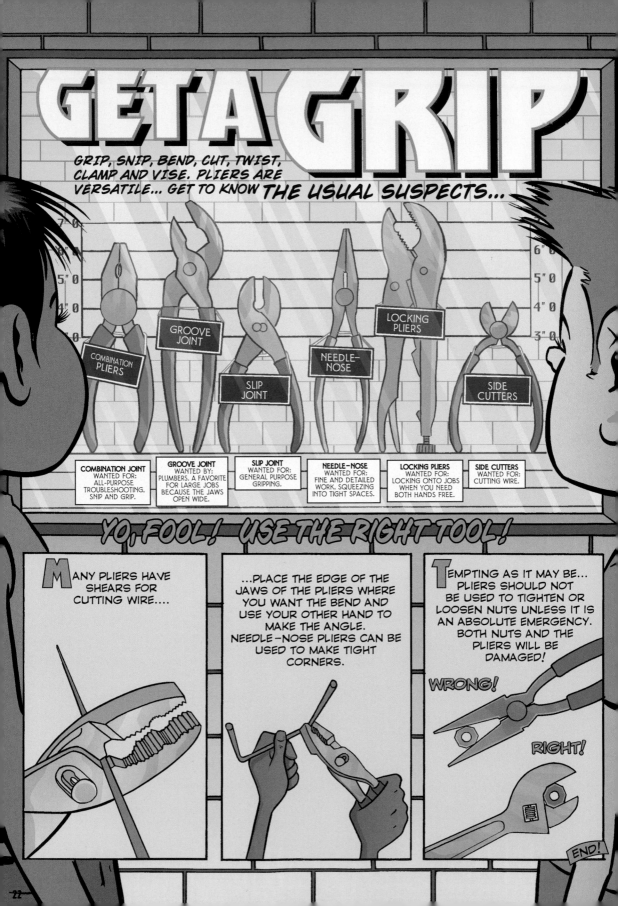

GET A GRIP

GRIP, SNIP, BEND, CUT, TWIST, CLAMP AND VISE. PLIERS ARE VERSATILE... GET TO KNOW **THE USUAL SUSPECTS...**

COMBINATION PLIERS

GROOVE JOINT

SLIP JOINT

NEEDLE-NOSE

LOCKING PLIERS

SIDE CUTTERS

COMBINATION JOINT
WANTED FOR: ALL-PURPOSE TROUBLESHOOTING, SNIP AND GRIP.

GROOVE JOINT
WANTED BY: PLUMBERS. A FAVORITE FOR LARGE JOBS BECAUSE THE JAWS OPEN WIDE.

SLIP JOINT
WANTED FOR: GENERAL PURPOSE GRIPPING.

NEEDLE-NOSE
WANTED FOR: FINE AND DETAILED WORK, SQUEEZING INTO TIGHT SPACES.

LOCKING PLIERS
WANTED FOR: LOCKING ONTO JOBS WHEN YOU NEED BOTH HANDS FREE.

SIDE CUTTERS
WANTED FOR: CUTTING WIRE.

YO, FOOL! USE THE RIGHT TOOL!

MANY PLIERS HAVE SHEARS FOR CUTTING WIRE....

...PLACE THE EDGE OF THE JAWS OF THE PLIERS WHERE YOU WANT THE BEND AND USE YOUR OTHER HAND TO MAKE THE ANGLE. NEEDLE-NOSE PLIERS CAN BE USED TO MAKE TIGHT CORNERS.

TEMPTING AS IT MAY BE... PLIERS SHOULD NOT BE USED TO TIGHTEN OR LOOSEN NUTS UNLESS IT IS AN ABSOLUTE EMERGENCY. BOTH NUTS AND THE PLIERS WILL BE DAMAGED!

WRONG!

RIGHT!

END!

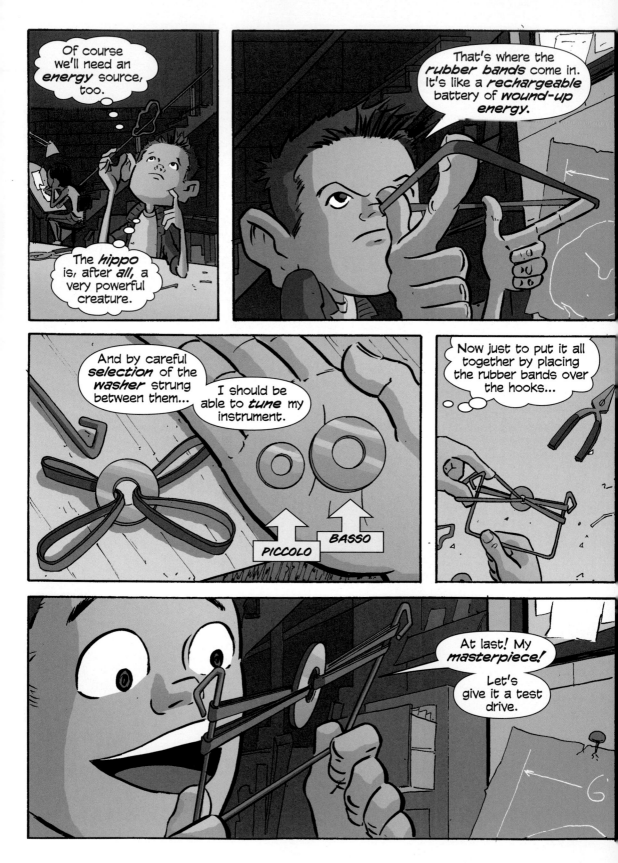

TOYS FROM TRASH

LAID OUT LIKE SO, ALL *I* HAD *TO DO* WAS *EXECUTE.*

CUT FOLD CUT FOLD CUT
CUT CUT
CUT CUT
FOLD CUT
FOLD FOLD
CUT CUT CUT

BEING WELL *PREPARED,* I WAS *CONFIDENT.* SUCCESS WAS A MATTER OF PATIENCE AND FOCUS.

I MADE THE CUTS *CAREFULLY,* THE FOLDS *PRECISELY.*

WITH CONFIDENCE I COULD NOW *IMPROVISE.* I MADE SLEEVES AND *TAPED* THE SEAMS SHUT WITH *DUCT TAPE.*

THE COAT WAS A PERFECT FIT.

NOW, WALKING THE STREETS I *CONTEMPLATED* THE *POSSIBILITIES.*

ALL THE DIFFERENT COATS THAT WERE *WITHIN* MY REACH.

TRASH BAG RAIN COAT

WHERE *OTHERS* HAD SEEN ONLY TRASH BAGS,

DUCT-TAPE SEAMS

RECEPTACLES *FIT* ONLY TO RECEIVE OUR *WASTE,*

I HAD SEEN SOMETHING DIFFERENT...

AND *IT* WAS BEAUTIFUL IN ITS SIMPLE *FUNCTION.*

CUT SLITS AND STRIPS FOR BELT.

THE *RAIN* LIGHTLY MASSAGED MY BRAIN.

IT WOULD BE *IMPERVIOUS* TO THE ELEMENTS THAT WOULD *IMPRISON* ME.

I WAS FREE.

APOLOGIES TO *FRANK MILLER!*

$$(prototyping + engineering)^{imagination} = better\ future$$

$$\left(\frac{dreaming^2 + experiment}{\sqrt{failure} \times renewal}\right) = invention$$

SPOOL RACER

$$passion + education + hard\ work > complacency$$

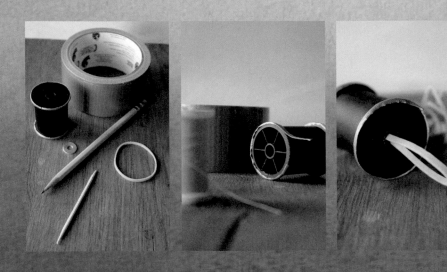

$$elegance = f(science,\ design)$$

$$instincts = \sum(experience\ +\ knowledge)$$

$$\int hard\ work\ d\ opportunity = success$$

$$\forall\ problems\ \exists\ a\ solution\ \in brain$$

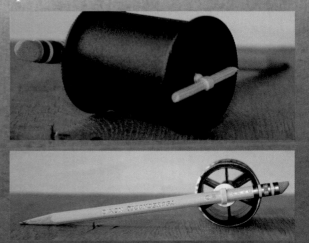

DRAGOTTA 2011

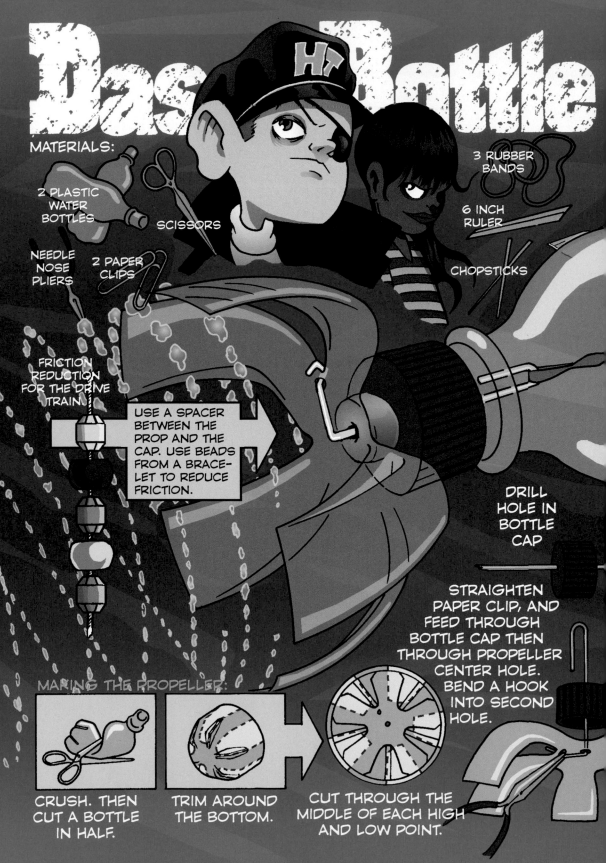

Das Bottle

MATERIALS:

2 PLASTIC WATER BOTTLES

SCISSORS

3 RUBBER BANDS

6 INCH RULER

NEEDLE NOSE PLIERS

2 PAPER CLIPS

CHOPSTICKS

FRICTION REDUCTION FOR THE DRIVE TRAIN.

USE A SPACER BETWEEN THE PROP AND THE CAP. USE BEADS FROM A BRACE-LET TO REDUCE FRICTION.

DRILL HOLE IN BOTTLE CAP

STRAIGHTEN PAPER CLIP, AND FEED THROUGH BOTTLE CAP THEN THROUGH PROPELLER CENTER HOLE. BEND A HOOK INTO SECOND HOLE.

MAKING THE PROPELLER:

CRUSH. THEN CUT A BOTTLE IN HALF.

TRIM AROUND THE BOTTOM.

CUT THROUGH THE MIDDLE OF EACH HIGH AND LOW POINT.

38

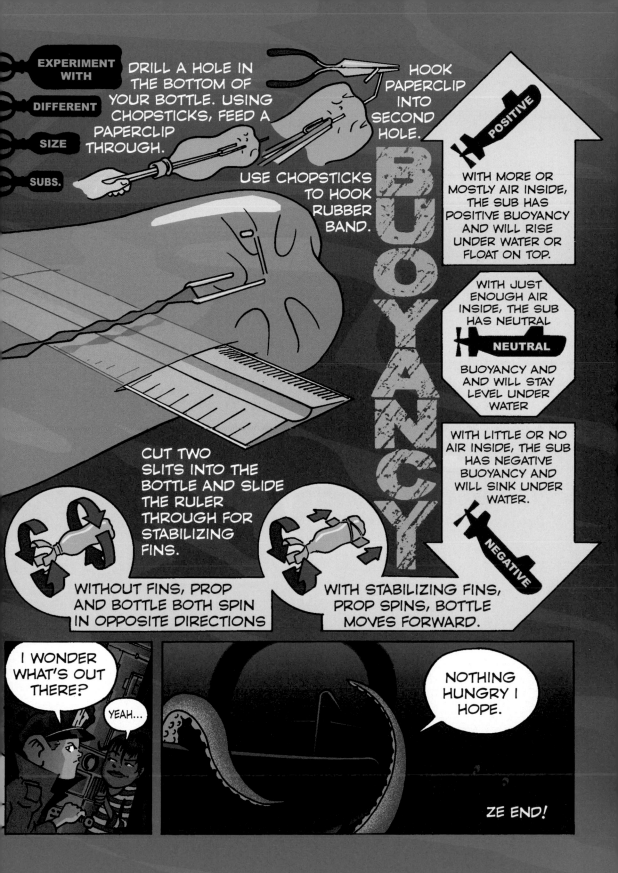

CAREFULLY CUT A 1/2" HOLE IN THE LOWER THIRD OF THE BOTTLE.

PUNCH OUT A HOLE IN A PIECE OF DUCT TAPE. ALIGN THE TWO HOLES AND STICK THE TAPE TO THE BOTTLE.

FIRST, POUR SEVERAL DROPS OF MILK INTO THE BOTTLE. THEN FILL WITH WATER. THE MIX SHOULD BE CLOUDY. PLUG THE HOLE WITH YOUR FINGER.

SCREW ON THE CAP OF BOTTLE AND REMOVE YOUR FINGER. THE WATER WILL STAY IN THE BOTTLE UNTIL MORE AIR IS LET IN THROUGH THE TOP.

TO GET A STEADY BEAM OF LIGHT USE A FLASH-LIGHT IN A BOX WITH PIN HOLE CUT IN IT. FOR OPTIMAL RESULTS, USE A LASER POINTER..

TWIST THE BOTTLE AND ALIGN THE BEAM SO IT SHINES THROUGH THE BOTTLE AND OUT THE HOLE.

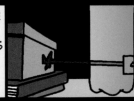

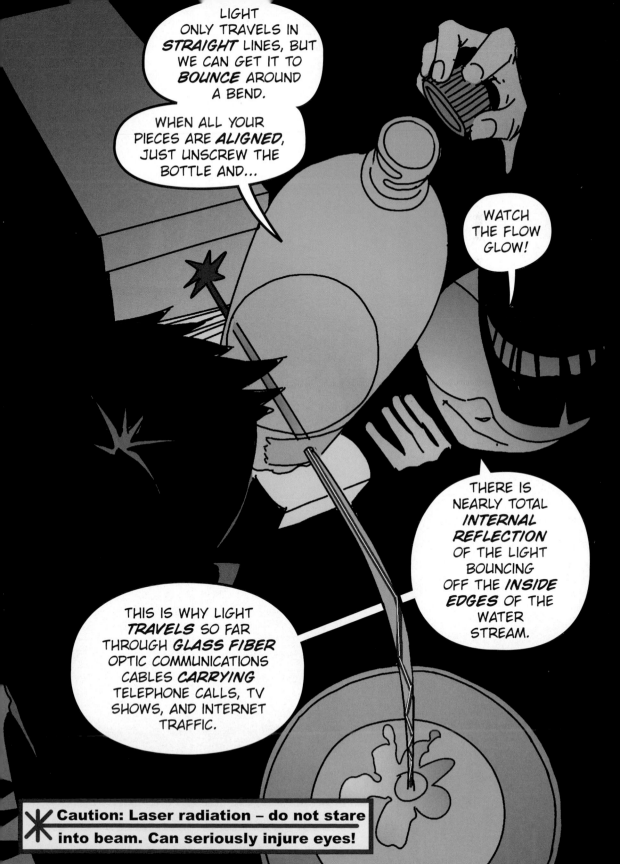

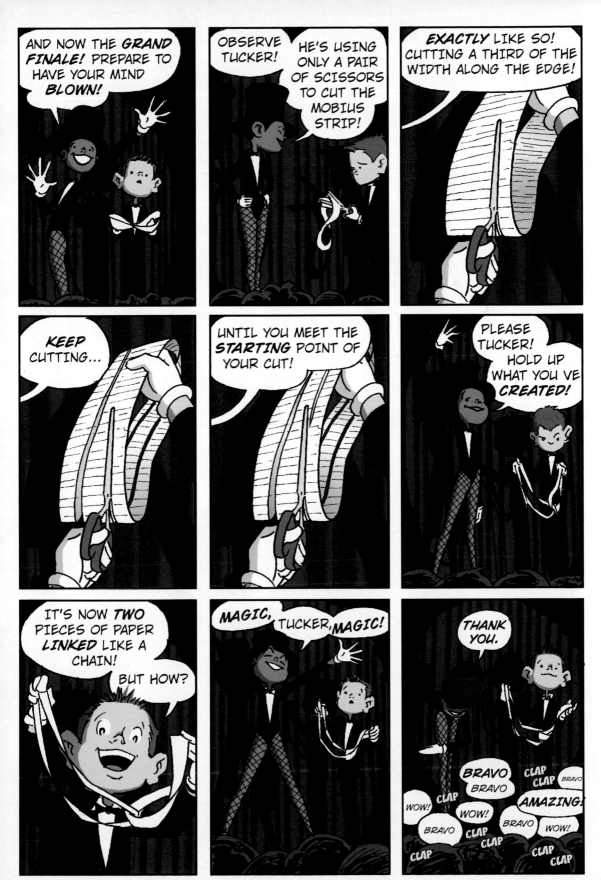

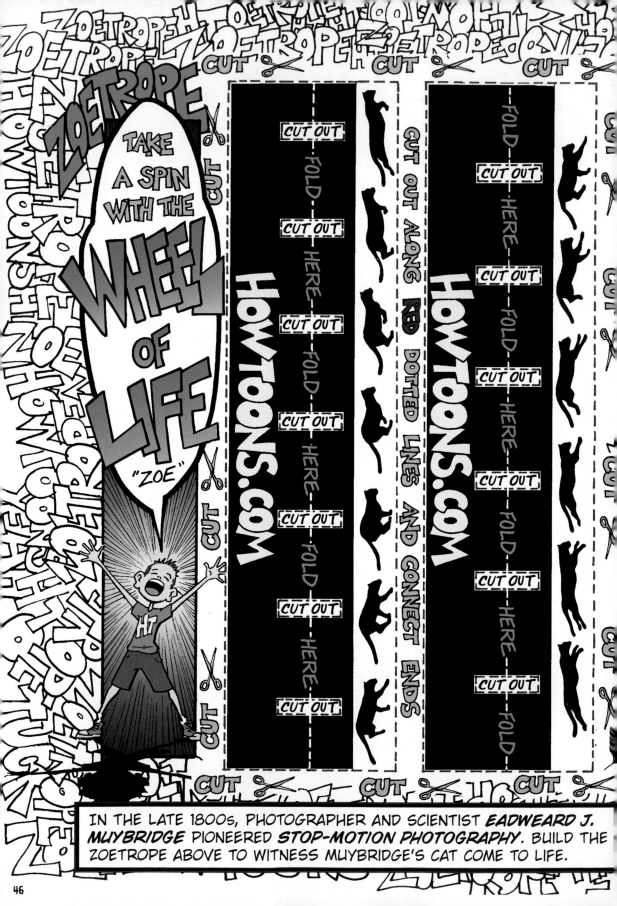

TAKE A SPIN WITH THE WHEEL OF LIFE "ZOE"

HowTOONS.com

HowTOONS.com

CUT OUT ALONG RED DOTTED LINES AND CONNECT ENDS

IN THE LATE 1800s, PHOTOGRAPHER AND SCIENTIST *EADWEARD J. MUYBRIDGE* PIONEERED *STOP-MOTION PHOTOGRAPHY*. BUILD THE ZOETROPE ABOVE TO WITNESS MUYBRIDGE'S CAT COME TO LIFE.

PHOTOCOPY THE STRIPS.

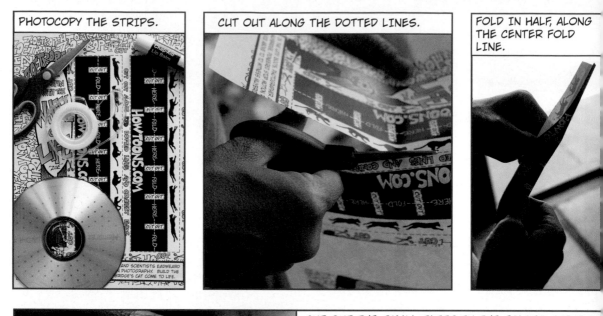

CUT OUT ALONG THE DOTTED LINES.

FOLD IN HALF, ALONG THE CENTER FOLD LINE.

CUT OUT THE SMALL SLITS IN THE FOLDED STRIPS TO CREATE PERSISTENCE OF VISION.

ATTACH STRIPS, OVERLAPPING THE TABS. ALIGN THE CORRECT CATS.

TAPE ONE SIDE...

THEN THE OTHER.

CENTER LOOPED STRIP ON TOP OF THE CD AND TAPE IT DOWN.

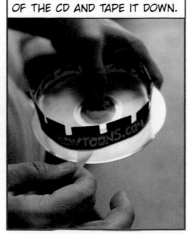

USE THE CHAPSTICK AS YOUR AXLE. CLOSE CAP TO FASTEN.

SPIN THE CD AND LOOK THROUGH THE SLITS TO THE CAT ON THE INSIDE. LOOKING THROUGH THE SLITS CREATES THE PHENOMENON KNOWN AS *PERSISTENCE OF VISION*.

HOWTOONS
CD HOVERCRAFT

MATERIALS:

BALLOON: FILLED WITH AIR, THIS IS YOUR BATTERY.

NOZZLE: THIS IS YOUR VALVE FOR CONTROLLING THE FLOW OF AIR.

FREE VALVE! ALWAYS BE ON THE LOOKOUT FOR USEFUL PROJECT PARTS IN EVERYDAY OBJECTS.

GLUE: HOLDS EVERYTHING TOGETHER.

CD: THIS IS YOUR HOVER-CRAFT BODY.

PLACE **BALLOON** OVER THE **NOZZLE**

GLUE NOZZLE TO **CD**

THE ELASTIC BALLOON *SLOWLY* RELEASES *PRESS-URIZED AIR* UNDER THE CD.

THIS AIR ACTS AS A *CUSHION, FLOATING* THE HOVERCRAFT A HAIR'S WIDTH *ABOVE* THE TABLE.

BECAUSE THERE IS *NO CONTACT* BETWEEN THE CD AND THE SURFACE, THERE IS ALMOST *NO FRICTION* AND THE HOVERCRAFT CAN *GLIDE* GRACEFULLY IN ANY DIRECTION.

BLOW IN AIR TO CHARGE UP YOUR BATTERY (BALLOON)

ON

OPEN VALVE

OFF

CLOSED VALVE

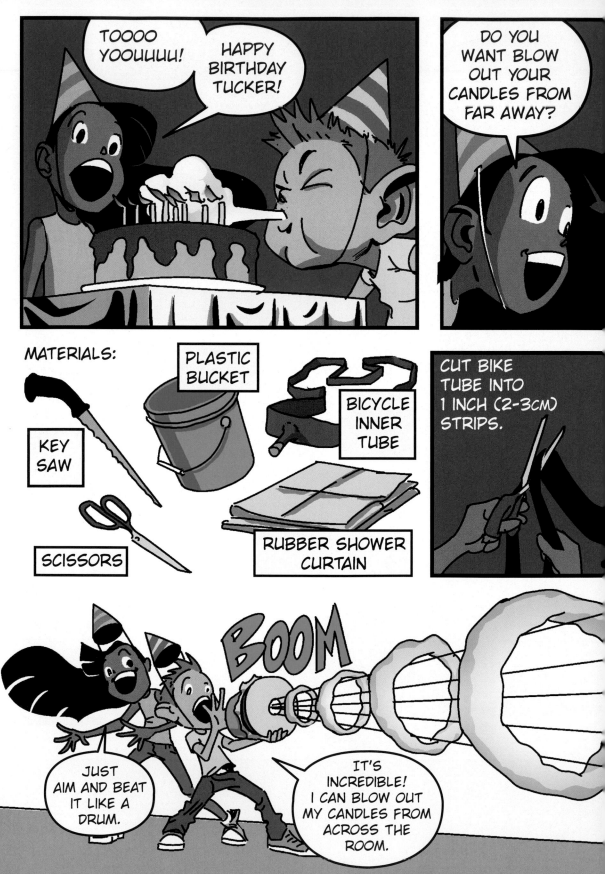

HOW ABOUT BLOWING CANDLES OUT FROM 10 FEET (3M).

OR EVEN UP TO 30 FEET (10M) AWAY. YOU CAN DO IT USING THE SHOCKWAVE AIR CANNON!

CUT 2 INCH (2-5CM) HOLE IN THE CENTER OF THE BUCKET'S BOTTOM.

PLACE THE SHOWER CURTAIN OVER THE TOP OF THE BUCKET.

STRETCH THE SHOWER CURTAIN AS TIGHT AS A DRUM OVER THE BUCKET. TIE IT DOWN WITH THE INNER TUBE STRIPS LIKE A BIG RUBBER BAND.

ADD FLOUR TO THE BUCKET TO CREATE SMOKE RINGS!

ROBOTS WITHIN REACH

THE SEARCH FOR A DEXTROUS ROBOTIC HAND HAS ELUDED ENGINEERS FOR DECADES. THE ANSWER IS AT YOUR FINGERTIPS!

HOWTOONS
THANKS ARVIND!

ROBOTIC HAND DESIGNED BY ARVIND GUPTA'S TOYS FROM TRASH. SEE MORE AT:
http://www.arvindguptatoys.com/toys.html

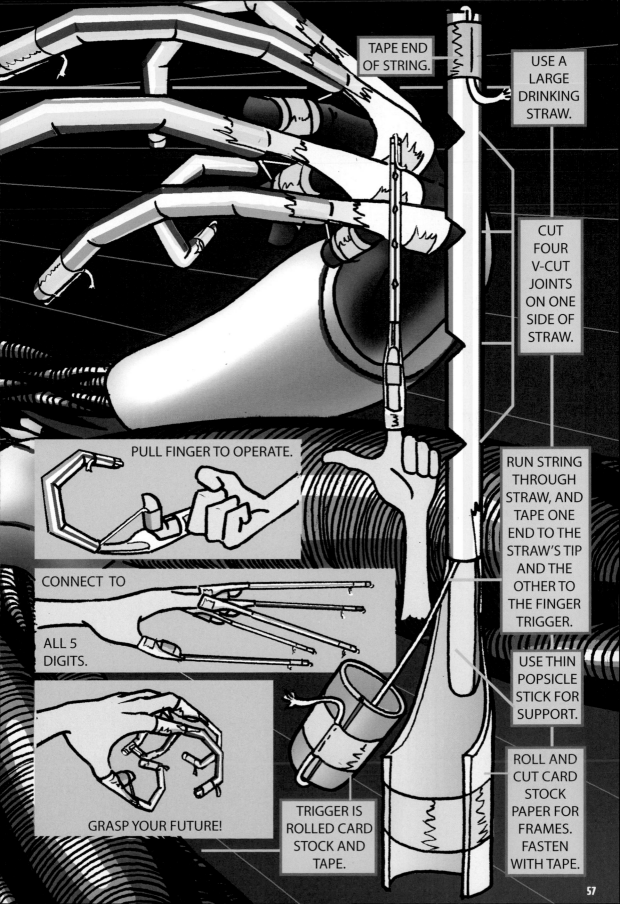

TAPE END OF STRING.

USE A LARGE DRINKING STRAW.

CUT FOUR V-CUT JOINTS ON ONE SIDE OF STRAW.

PULL FINGER TO OPERATE.

RUN STRING THROUGH STRAW, AND TAPE ONE END TO THE STRAW'S TIP AND THE OTHER TO THE FINGER TRIGGER.

CONNECT TO

ALL 5 DIGITS.

USE THIN POPSICLE STICK FOR SUPPORT.

ROLL AND CUT CARD STOCK PAPER FOR FRAMES. FASTEN WITH TAPE.

GRASP YOUR FUTURE!

TRIGGER IS ROLLED CARD STOCK AND TAPE.

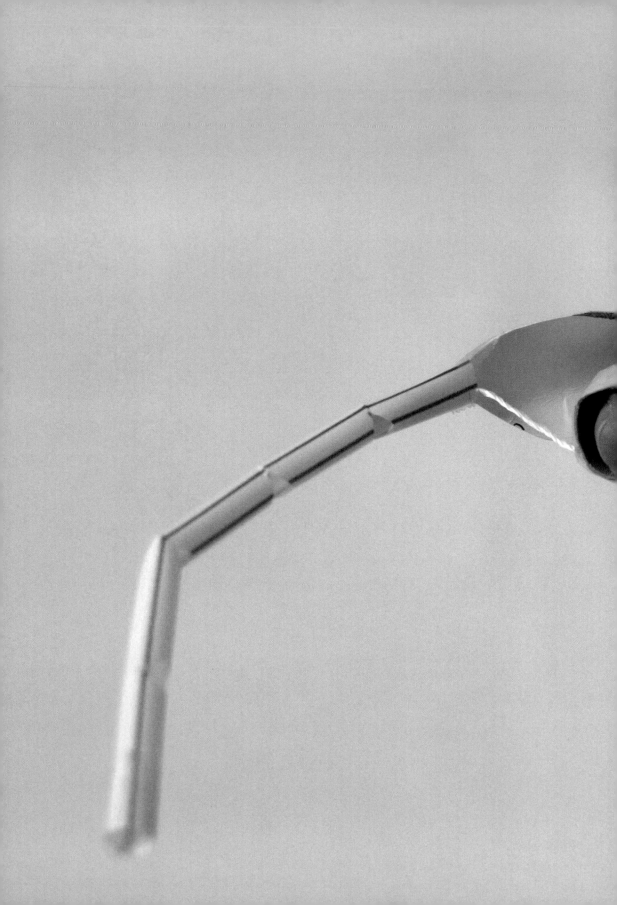

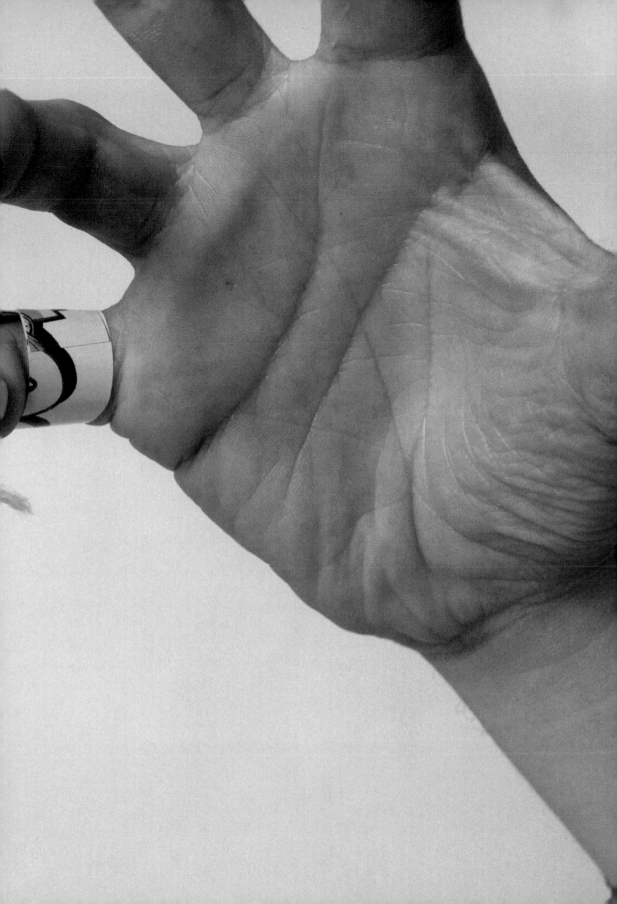

ROBO-ARM

AGHHHH... ALMOST... GOT... ONE!

HERE TUCK, LET ME *EXTEND* YOU A HAND!

THE *ROBOTIC ARM* CREATES COORDINATED MOTIONS WHICH MOVE IN WAYS THAT OUR ARM CAN'T.

BY MAKING *INTELLIGENT MECHANISMS* THAT EXTEND OUR CAPABILITIES WE CAN DO TASKS THAT ARE NORMALLY *BEYOND* OUR REACH.

DRILL 3/16" HOLES THROUGH THE 9" PAINT STICKS.

1"
3.5"
3.5"
1"

CONNECT THE PAINT STICKS TOGETHER.

8-32 X 1/4" MACHINE SCREW

#8-32 WASHE

#8-32 HEX NUT

CROSS AND CONNECT STICKS IN THE MIDDLE.

CUT TWO 2"X4" SECTION FROM A GROUT SPONGE.

SLICE THE SPONGE IN THE MIDDLE AND SLIDE STICK THROUGH.

PULLING IN, WILL EXTEND THE ROBO-ARM OUT; CLOSING THE SPONGE GRIPPERS.

YOU CAN EXPERIMENT WITH THE GRIPPER'S LENGTH. TOO MANY STICKS WILL CAUSE THE GRIPPER TO SAG.

PUSHING THE STICKS OUT WILL RETRACT ROBO-ARM.

THE PNEUMATIC KIDS

WOW!

WE WOULDN'T NEED TECHNOLOGY IF *SUPERPOWERS* WERE REALLY POSSIBLE!

TO GAIN EXTRA STRENGTH, WE NEED MORE *MUSCLES*, OR *"ACTUATORS"* AS TECHIES CALL THEM.

TO *POWER* OUR MUSCLES, WE CAN DEVELOP NEW *PNEUMATIC* TECHNOLOGIES OR *AIR-POWERED* MUSCLES.

WE CAN MAKE THESE *PNEUMATIC MUSCLES* BY USING PRESSURIZED *AIR* CANISTERS CONNECTED TO A NETWORK OF HOSES THAT *ADD* AND *SUBTRACT* AIR, MOVING THE 23 DIFFERENT MUSCLES OF THE ARM.

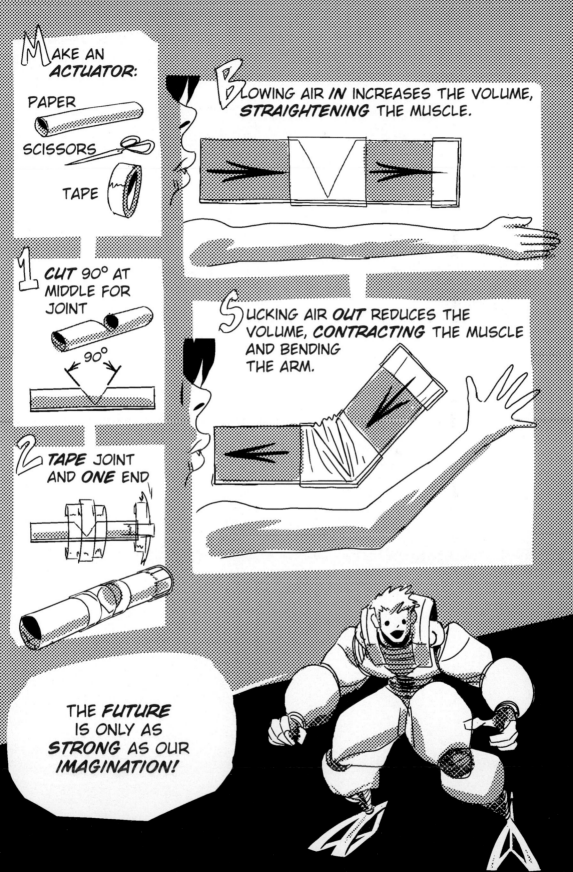

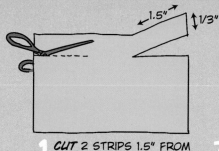 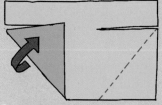 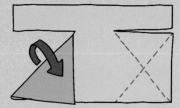

1 *CUT* 2 STRIPS 1.5" FROM EACH SIDE 1/3" DOWN

2 *VALLEY-FOLD* CORNERS UP TO MEET CUT LINES CREATING A VALLEY CREASE.

3 *VALLEY-FOLD* TOP CORNER DOWN CREATING A DIAGONAL.

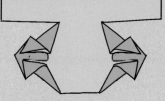 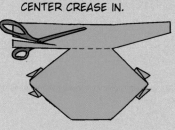 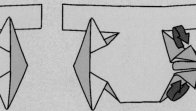 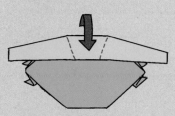

4 FOLD IN HALF ALONG THE CREASE AND *TURN OVER* AND REPEAT.

5 CREATE A *COLLAPSABLE FOLD* BY *PINCHING* THE CENTER CREASE IN.

6 FOLD *CORNER POINTS* UPWARDS TO MAKE YOUR *LEGS*.

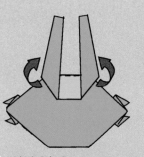 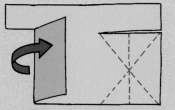

7 *REPEAT* WITH THE OTHER SIDE.

8 *SHAPE* YOUR *ANTENNAS* BY *CUTTING* DIAGONAL LINES.

9 *VALLEY-FOLD* ANTENNA UP ALONG THE CUT LINES.

10 *VALLEY-FOLD* ANTENNAS UP.

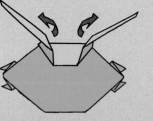

11 *MOUNTAIN-FOLD* ANTENNAS DOWN.

12 PUT IT *TOGETHER!*

TAPE

STRIP WIRE FROM VIBRATION MOTOR.

BATTERY

FOAM TAPE

*PRESS DOWN ON THE GAMI-BOT TO EVEN THE SURFACE AREA OF LEGS AND HELP THE BOT GO STRAIGHT.

PLAY WITH YOUR FOOD

FROM THE *GLACIERS* OF NORWAY THEY CUT THE PUREST *BLOCKS* OF ICE, A *DELICACY* IN WARMER CLIMATES — THEY HAD TO MOVE *QUICKLY* WITH THEIR PRECIOUS QUARRY...

THEY FOUND *SUGAR* IN PERSIA, A VALUABLE COMMODITY THAT HAD MADE ITS WAY FROM *NEW GUINEA* VIA *INDIA* AND *CHINA*...

SUGAR

FROM *SPANISH* CONQUISTADORS THEY RECEIVED SOME OF THE FIRST SAMPLES OF THE VERSATILE *VANILLA BEAN* THAT WAS BEING CULTIVATED IN *MEXICO.*

IN NORTHERN EUROPE THEY FOUND THE *FRESHEST MILK* AND DIVINED THE SECRETS OF MAKING THE *THICKEST* CREAM!

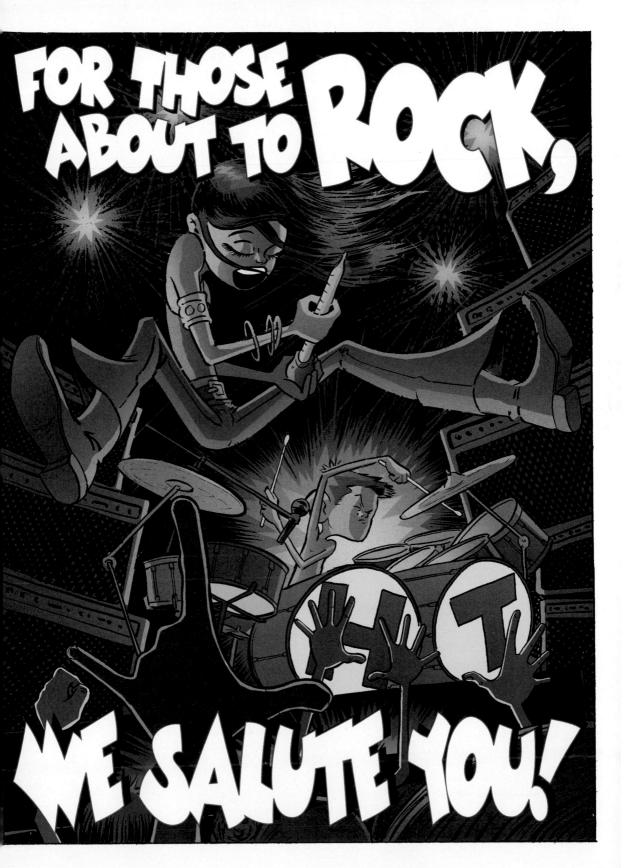

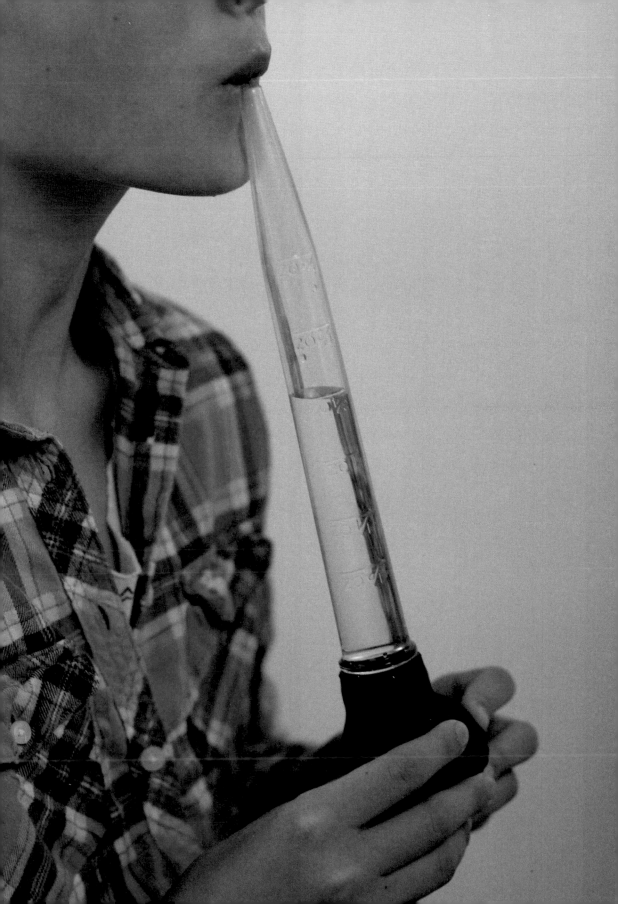

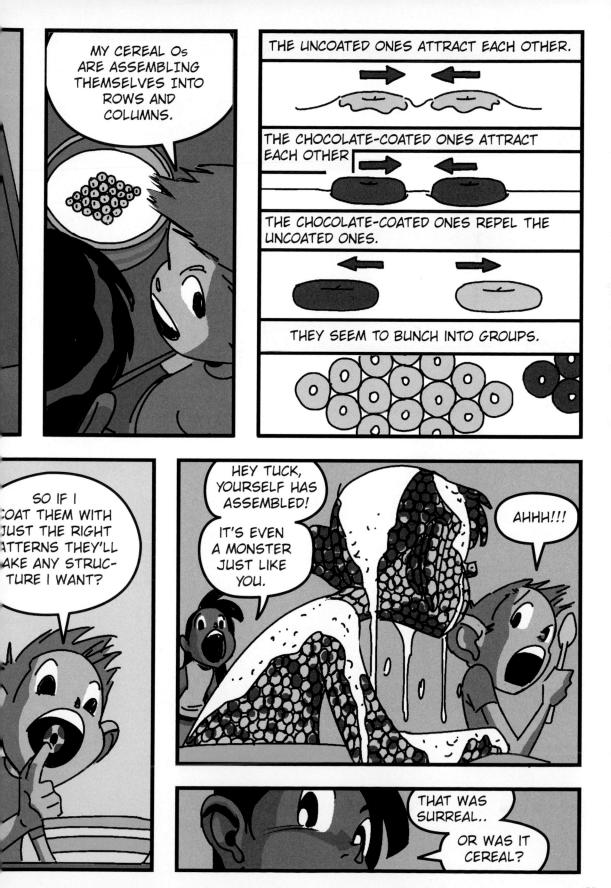

ハウー
チューンズ

SPRING-LOADED   CHOPSTICKS

DŌMO

ARIGATŌ

TUCKER

SAN.

USE CHOPSTICKS AND CLOTHES PIN.   REPLACE WOOD OF CLOTHES PIN WITH CHOPSTICK.

SPRING-LOADED CHOPSTICKS HAVE MANY USES SUCH AS EATING UTENSILS AND TWEEZERS.

NICK DRAGOTTA · JOOST BONSEN · SAUL GRIFFITH

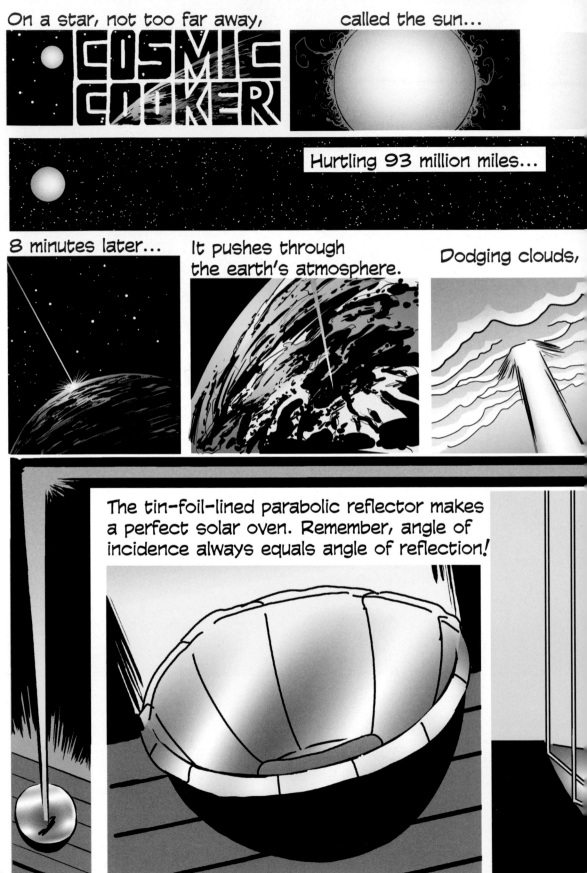

A photon begins its journey...

at the speed of light.

narrowly missing dust particles. Its journey continues until its purpose is complete.

Its purpose... LIFE!

Activity, impulse, liveliness, zest...

ENERGY!

Put the bowl directly in the sun, and the sun's rays will focus at a single point.

The photons hit the atoms in your dog, and cause them to vibrate.

The light is converted to heat. The heat cooks the proteins in the hotdog.

Allow hotdog to cook for at least 45 minutes or until the hotdog reaches 160°.

This hotdog is out of this world!

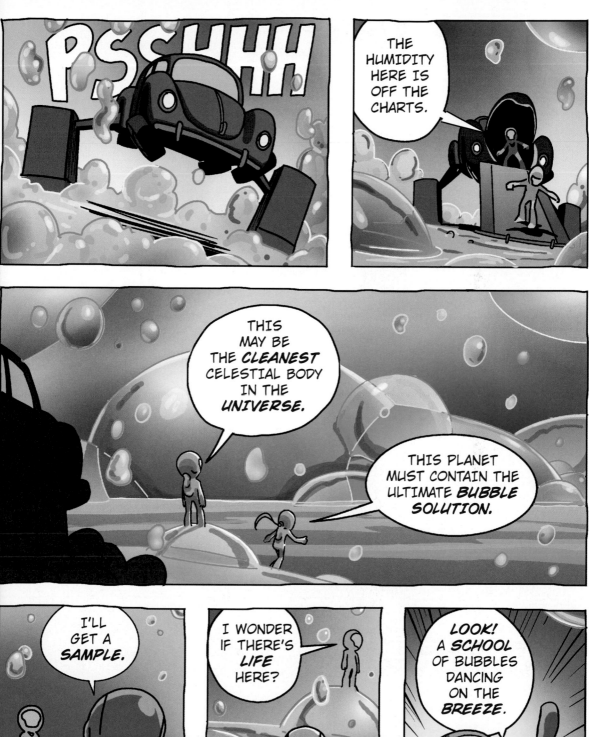

BACK AT THE LAB, THE SCIENTIFIC METHOD BEGINS.

CELINE COLLECTS DATA THROUGH OBSERVATION AND EXPERIMENTATION, FORMULATING AND TESTING HER HYPOTHESIS.

UNTIL...

BUBBLES!

YOU *DID* IT CELINE!

THE *KEY* WAS TO REALIZE THAT THE SOAP FORMS A *SKIN* LAYER ON EITHER SIDE OF THE WATER.

"BUBBLES EXIST WHEN THE *AIR PRESSURE* INSIDE THE BUBBLE IS IN PERFECT *BALANCE* WITH THE AIR PRESSURE *OUTSIDE* OF THE BUBBLE."

"THE SOAP, CALLED A *LIPID*, MAKES A THIN LAYER PROTECTING THE WATER."

ONE LAYER ON EACH SIDE IS WHY SCIENTISTS CALL THIS A LIPID BILAYER."

LIPID
WATER
LIPID

"I BROKE DOWN THE *INGREDIENTS* FOR..."

(THE ULTIMATE) BUBBLE SOLUTION

—10 CUPS OF WATER
—1 CUP OF DISH SOAP
—1/4 CUP OF GLYCERIN (PURCHASE AT DRUG STORE)

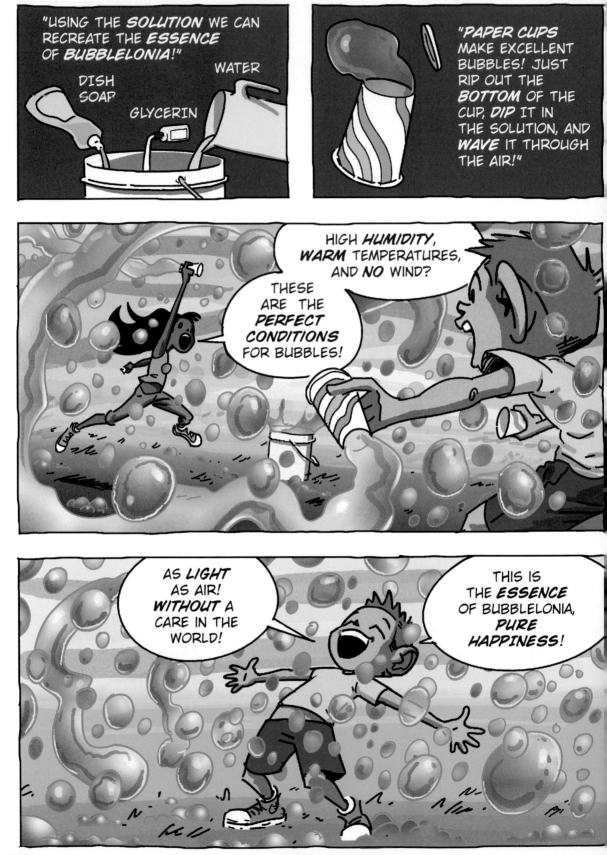

105

TERRARIUM

I'm going to need a spacecraft that can support human life for long periods of time without resupply ships...
And scientists haven't yet figured out how to create such a complex ecosystem. It's hard, like trying to make a miniature world...
And we humans haven't exactly figured out how not to pollute Earth, either...
So I'm practicing here in my...
TERRARIUM!

A NICE BIG PICKLE JAR WITH A LID WILL WORK NICELY. YOU COULD USE A FISH TANK, OR EVEN A LARGE SODA BOTTLE WITH THE TOP CUT OFF.

P LACE A FEW INCHES OF DIRT IN THE JAR, WITH PEBBLES ON THE BOTTOM TO GIVE IT BETTER DRAINAGE.

F ILL THE TERRARIUM WITH EVERYDAY THINGS YOU FIND IN NATURE: ROCKS, STICKS, WORMS AND INSECTS. IF YOU BUILD A REALLY LARGE ONE, YOU CAN TRY SMALL LIZARDS.

S MALL SHADE AND WATER-LOVING PLANTS ARE BEST, LIKE CLOVER OR SMALL FERNS. MOSSES AND LICHEN WORK VERY WELL, TOO!

B UT BEWARE! CREATURES NEED TO EAT! IF YOUR TERRARIUM CAN'T SUPPLY ENOUGH NUTRIENTS, YOU WILL HAVE TO FEED THEM.

P LACE THE JAR WHERE IT WILL RECEIVE PARTIAL SUNLIGHT. WATER ONCE IN THE BEGINNING, BUT NOT TOO MUCH, OR THE PLANTS WILL ROT. THE WATER VAPOR WILL STAY IN THE JAR AND BE CONTINUALLY RECYCLED.

Y OU CAN LEAVE THE TERRARIUM OPEN AT THE TOP BY PUTTING SMALL HOLES IN THE LID. THIS WAY IT CAN GET NUTRIENTS FROM THE OUTSIDE WORLD AND SURVIVE A LONG TIME. IF YOU SEAL IT COMPLETELY, YOU ARE RUNNING AN EXPERIMENT IN CLOSED ECOSYSTEMS. THE NUTRIENTS FROM THE SOIL FEED THE PLANTS, AND THE NUTRIENTS FROM THE PLANTS FEED THE INSECTS, AND THE CARBON DIOXIDE NEEDED BY ALL LIVING THINGS WILL HAVE TO BE BALANCED PERFECTLY BY THE WHOLE SYSTEM.

THE BUGEYE LENS

I LOVE ENTOMOLOGY.

| USING A SAFETY PIN WE CAN CONSTRUCT A WATER DROPLET LENS. | DIP THE LOOP END INTO WATER. | LOOP SIZE DETERMINES DROPLET SIZE AND THUS MAGNIFACATION | YOU CAN HOLD OR MOUNT THE SAFETY PIN. BY TWISTING THE CAP I CAN GRADUALLY ADJUST THE FOCUS FOR MY LENS. |

LOWER OR RAISE TO FOCUS

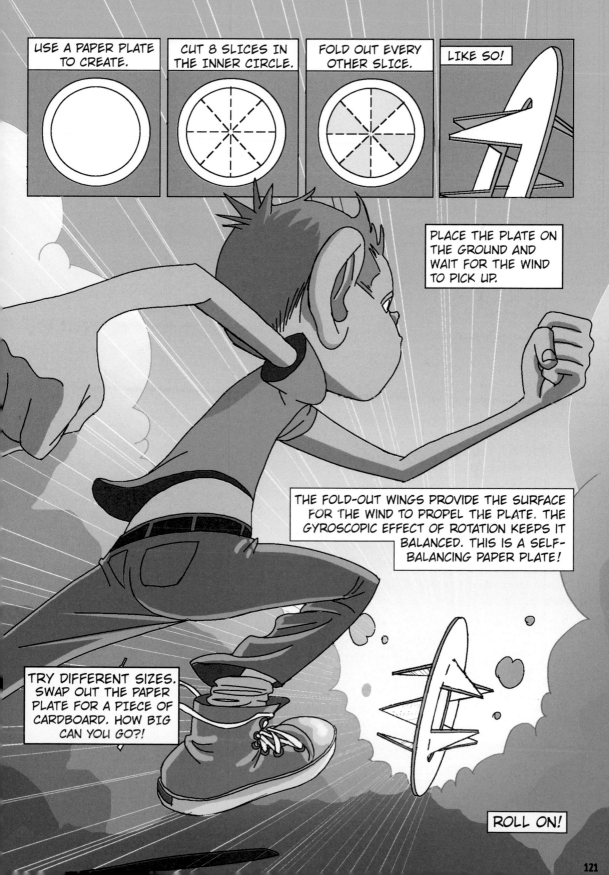

USE A PAPER PLATE TO CREATE.

CUT 8 SLICES IN THE INNER CIRCLE.

FOLD OUT EVERY OTHER SLICE.

LIKE SO!

PLACE THE PLATE ON THE GROUND AND WAIT FOR THE WIND TO PICK UP.

THE FOLD-OUT WINGS PROVIDE THE SURFACE FOR THE WIND TO PROPEL THE PLATE. THE GYROSCOPIC EFFECT OF ROTATION KEEPS IT BALANCED. THIS IS A SELF-BALANCING PAPER PLATE!

TRY DIFFERENT SIZES. SWAP OUT THE PAPER PLATE FOR A PIECE OF CARDBOARD. HOW BIG CAN YOU GO?!

ROLL ON!

TAKE FLIGHT

Stomp ROCKET

MAKE THE LAUNCHER

PVC PIPE IS A VERSATILE MATERIAL FOUND AT ANY HARDWARE STORE. USE 60" OF 1/2" INTERNAL DIAMETER PVC PIPE.

CUT YOUR PIPE TO THE SPECS BELOW.

60"

18"

24"

6" 6" 6"

2 END CAPS

CROSS JOINT

ELBOW JOINT

18"

6"

6"

6"

6"

RECYCLE A 2 LITER SODA BOTTLE TO GENERATE THE FORCE!

24"

PUT THE PIPE 2" INTO THE SODA BOTTLE AND TAPE THEM TOGETHER USING DUCT TAPE.

ANGLE YOUR LAUNCHER ANY DEGREE YOU WANT.

SHOOT IT UP, OR ARC IT!

AFTER YOU MAKE THE ROCKET, STOMP THE BOTTLE AND WATCH IT FLY!

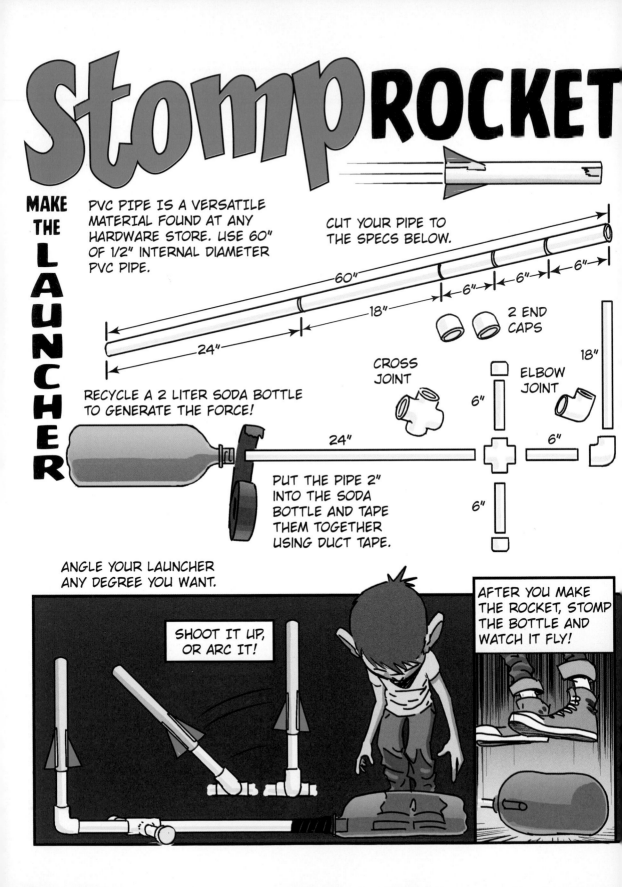

126

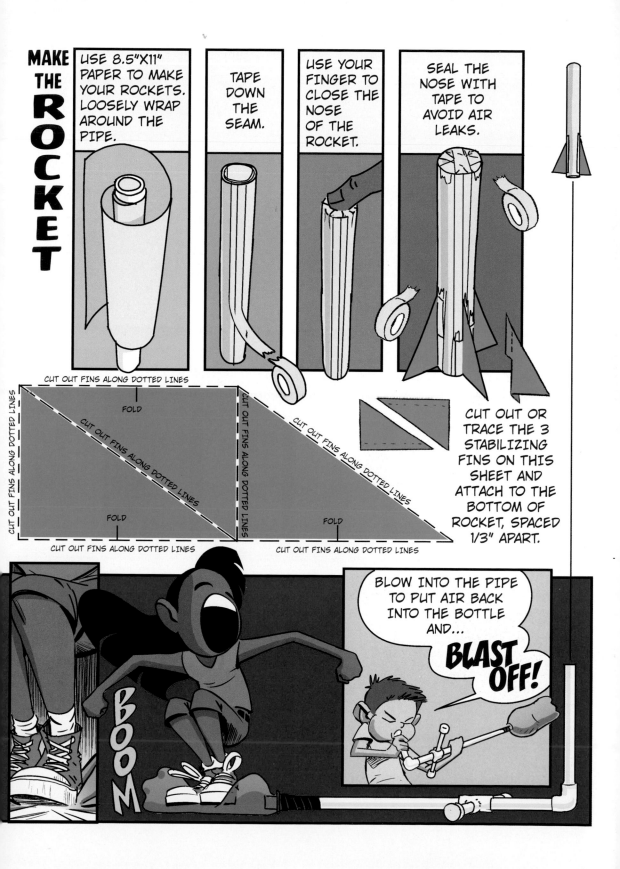

MAKE THE **ROCKET**

USE 8.5"X11" PAPER TO MAKE YOUR ROCKETS. LOOSELY WRAP AROUND THE PIPE.

TAPE DOWN THE SEAM.

USE YOUR FINGER TO CLOSE THE NOSE OF THE ROCKET.

SEAL THE NOSE WITH TAPE TO AVOID AIR LEAKS.

CUT OUT FINS ALONG DOTTED LINES

FOLD

CUT OUT FINS ALONG DOTTED LINES

CUT OUT FINS ALONG DOTTED LINES

CUT OUT FINS ALONG DOTTED LINES

CUT OUT FINS ALONG DOTTED LINES

FOLD

FOLD

CUT OUT FINS ALONG DOTTED LINES

CUT OUT FINS ALONG DOTTED LINES

CUT OUT OR TRACE THE 3 STABILIZING FINS ON THIS SHEET AND ATTACH TO THE BOTTOM OF ROCKET, SPACED 1/3" APART.

BLOW INTO THE PIPE TO PUT AIR BACK INTO THE BOTTLE AND...

BLAST OFF!

BOOM

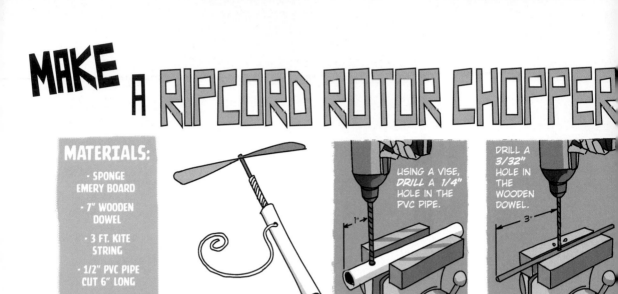

MAKE A RIPCORD ROTOR CHOPPER

MATERIALS:

- SPONGE EMERY BOARD
- 7" WOODEN DOWEL
- 3 FT. KITE STRING
- 1/2" PVC PIPE CUT 6" LONG

USING A VISE, *DRILL* A *1/4"* HOLE IN THE PVC PIPE.

DRILL A *3/32"* HOLE IN THE WOODEN DOWEL.

CUT A HOLE THROUGH THE EMERY BOARD AND GLUE THE WOODEN DOWEL TO THE BOARD.

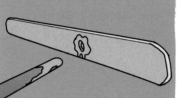

LET THE GLUE DRY. *TWIST* THE EMERY BOARD TO GIVE THE ROTOR *LIFT*.

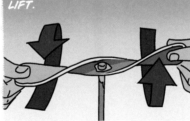

THREAD THE STRING THROUGH THE PVC PIPE AND WOODEN DOWEL LIKE SO.

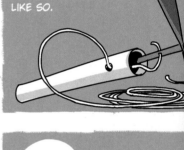

SPIN THE ROTOR *COUNTER-CLOCKWISE* TO WIND THE STRING AROUND THE DOWEL.

GRIP IT...

AND *RIP* IT.

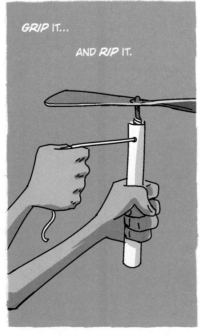

GIVE IT A *WHIRL!*

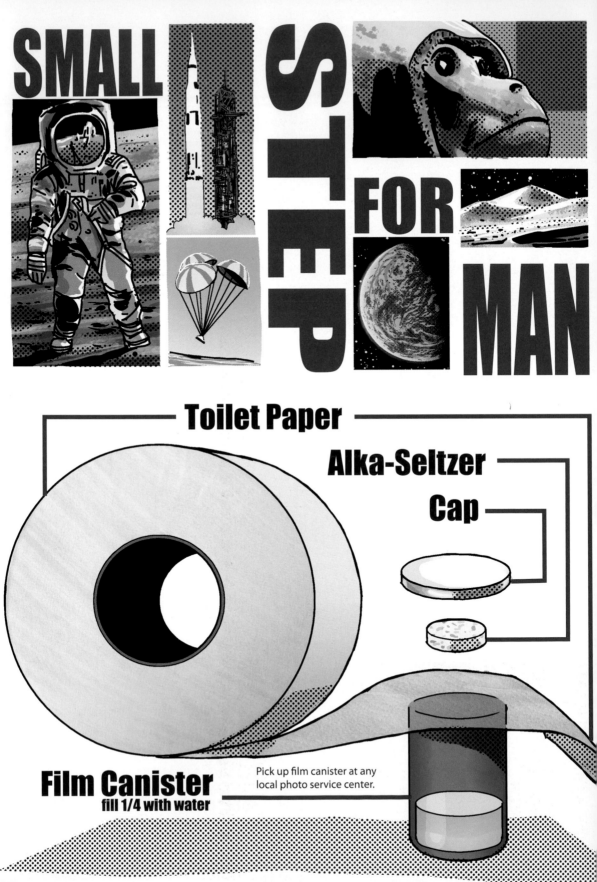

SMALL STEP FOR MAN

Toilet Paper

Alka-Seltzer

Cap

Film Canister
fill 1/4 with water

Pick up film canister at any local photo service center.

CLOSE THE LID

TEAR AWAY EXCESS T.P.

FLIP OVER

Alka-Seltzer tablets contain citric acid and sodium bicarbonate. When dropped in water the two ingredients mix, causing a chemical reaction that produces the CO_2 gas. The gas builds until the bottle can't contain it anymore, thus Newton's 3rd law.

"For every action there is an equal and opposite reaction."

Sir Isaac Newton

POP

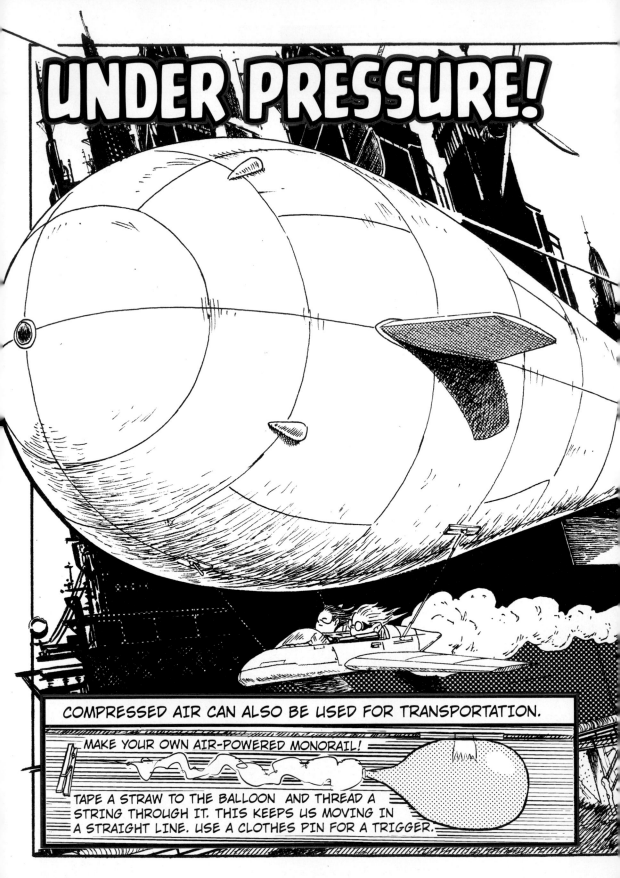

UNDER PRESSURE!

COMPRESSED AIR CAN ALSO BE USED FOR TRANSPORTATION.

MAKE YOUR OWN AIR-POWERED MONORAIL!

TAPE A STRAW TO THE BALLOON AND THREAD A STRING THROUGH IT. THIS KEEPS US MOVING IN A STRAIGHT LINE. USE A CLOTHES PIN FOR A TRIGGER.

NOW COMPRESSED AIR CAN BE USED TO POWER THE FUTURE:

SOLAR-POWERED AIR COMPRESSOR COMPRESSES AIR AND PUSHES IT INTO UNDER-GROUND TANKS.

HIGH-PRESSURE AIR IS LIKE A BATTERY. THE ENERGY CAN BE RELEASED LATER TO DRIVE A TURBINE.

AIR PRESSURE SPINS A TURBINE WHICH DRIVES A GENERATOR TO MAKE ELECTRICITY.

THE RIGHTEOUS STUFF

GO WHERE NO KID HAS GONE BEFORE

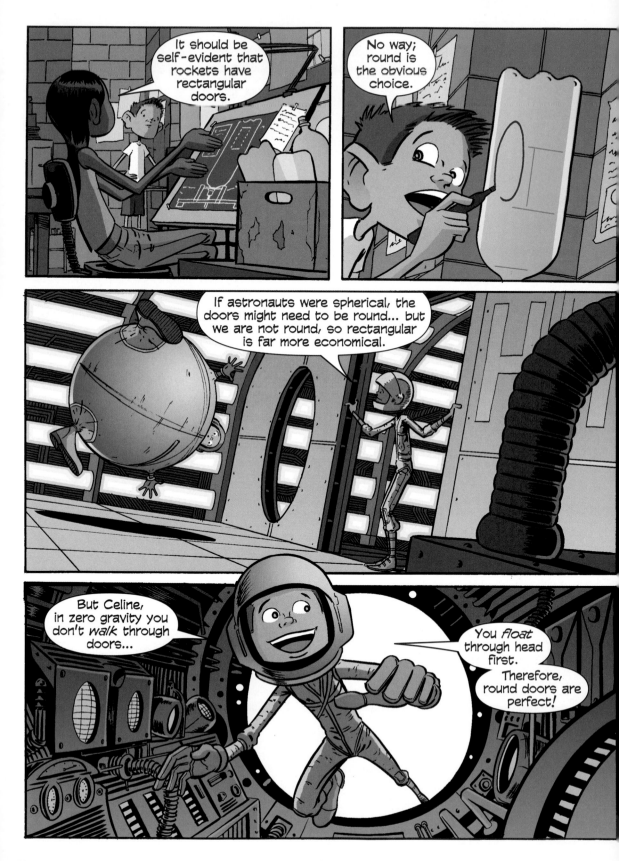

I'll launch first.

Fine! Let's set 'em up.

Ready, Tuck?

My systems are go.

Me too!

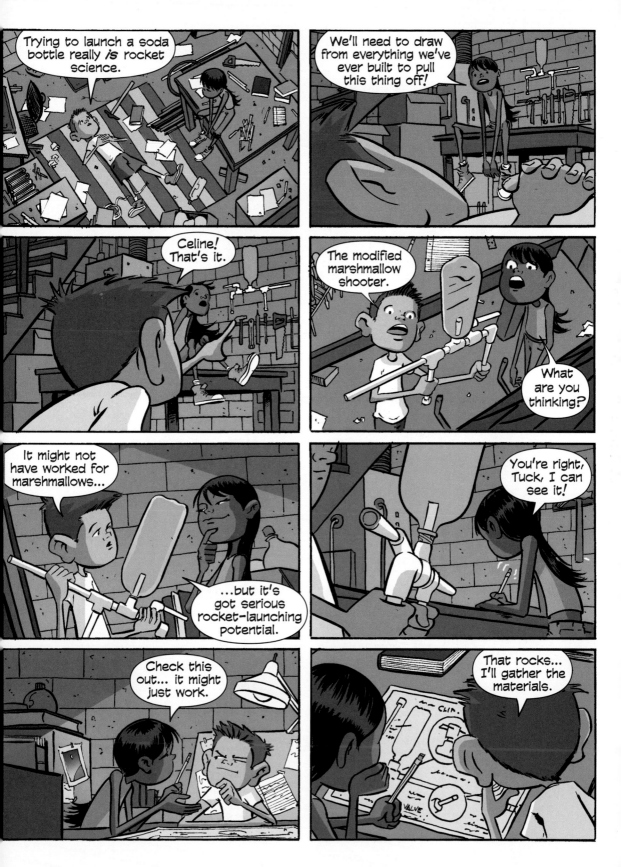

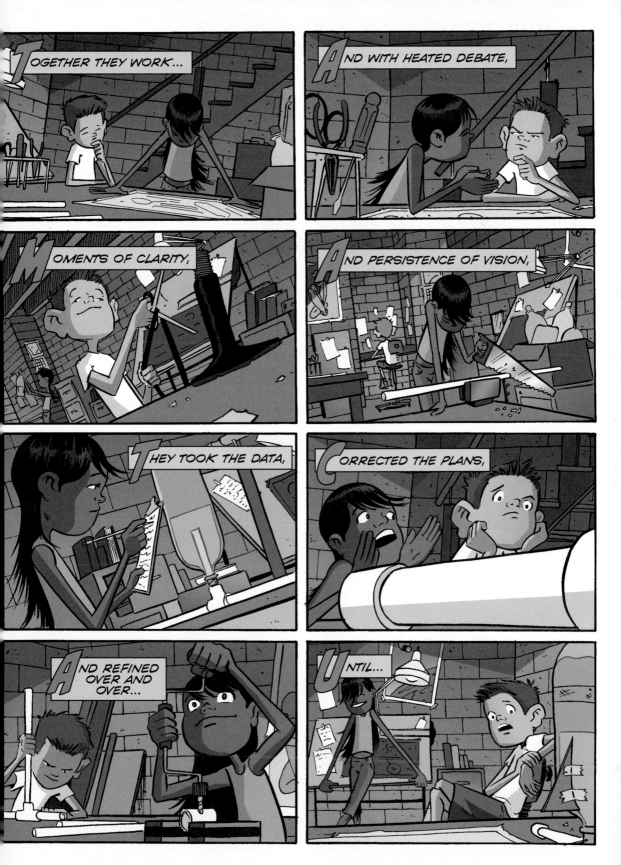

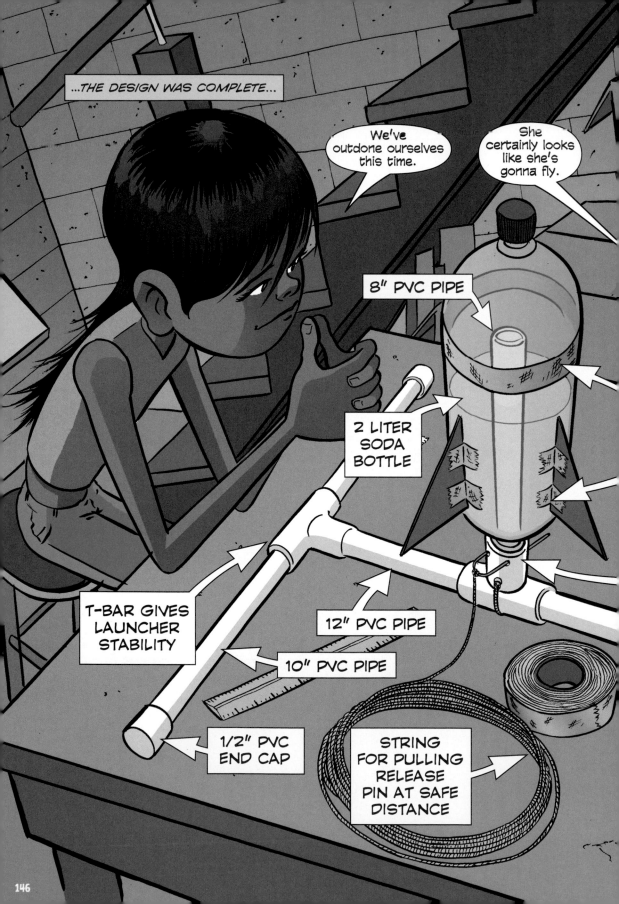

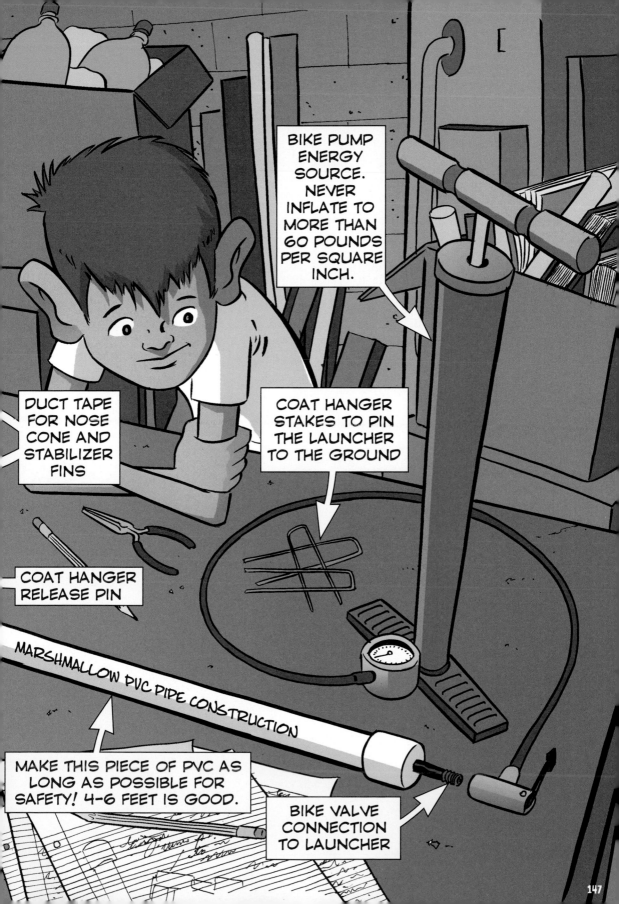

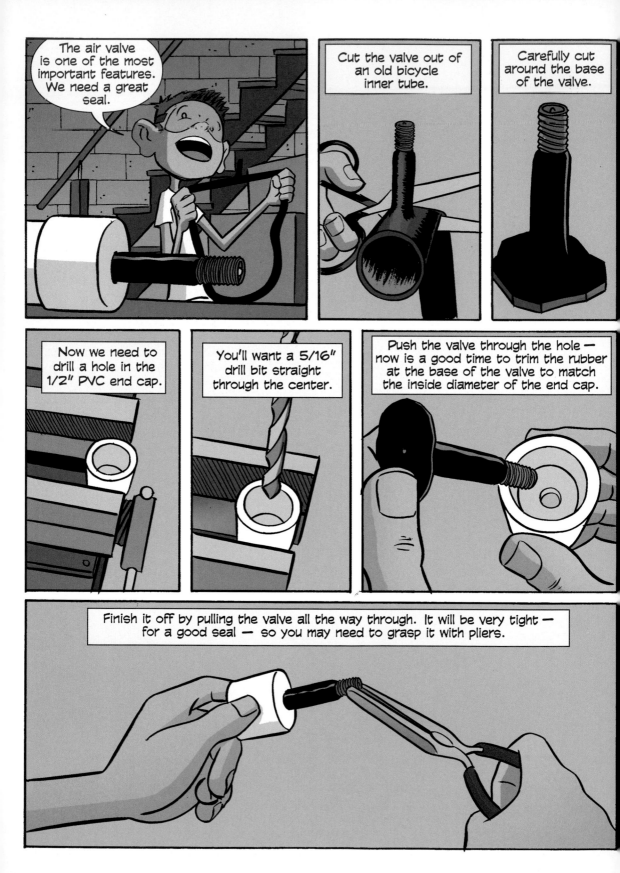

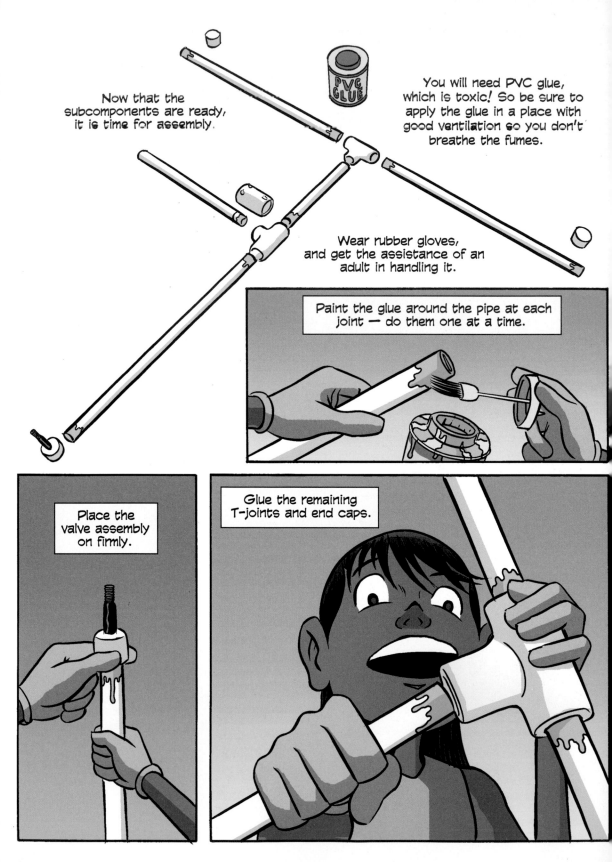

Now that the subcomponents are ready, it is time for assembly.

You will need PVC glue, which is toxic! So be sure to apply the glue in a place with good ventilation so you don't breathe the fumes.

Wear rubber gloves, and get the assistance of an adult in handling it.

Paint the glue around the pipe at each joint — do them one at a time.

Place the valve assembly on firmly.

Glue the remaining T-joints and end caps.

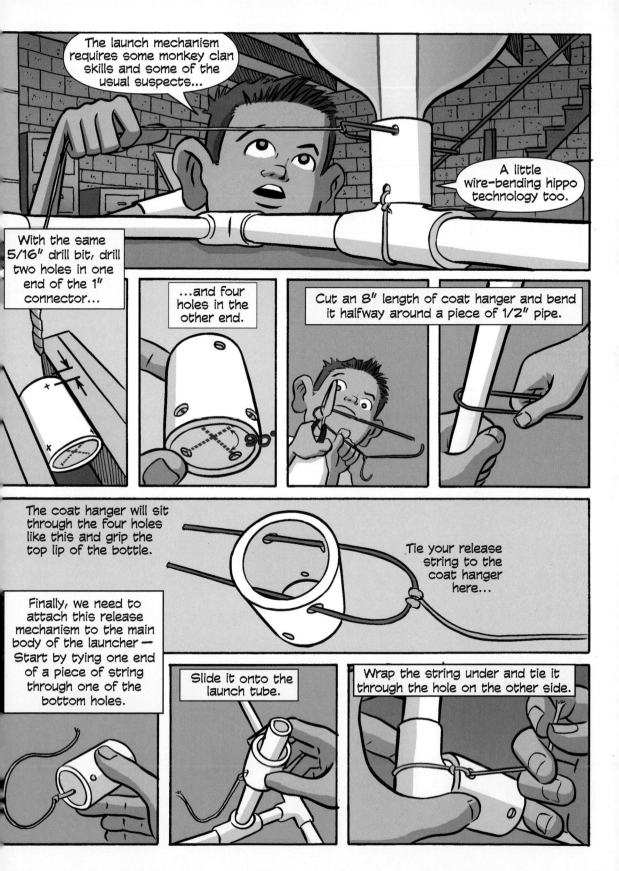

And of course the last thing you'll need is a rocket!

You can leave a message in your bottle for the aliens who will find it once it reaches orbit — or you can figure out a way to pack a parachute in there.

For the aerodynamic nose cone, cut the top off a second bottle...

And tape it around the bottom of the main bottle.

For the fins, cut some fin shapes from cardboard...

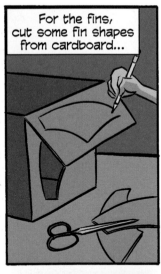

...and tape them firmly to the outside of the bottle.

The stabilizing fins should be symmetrical and aligned with the flight direction!

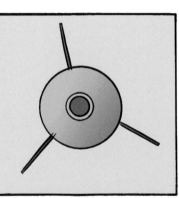

And after all that work, we can finally fill the rocket with the power source — plain tap water will do.

152

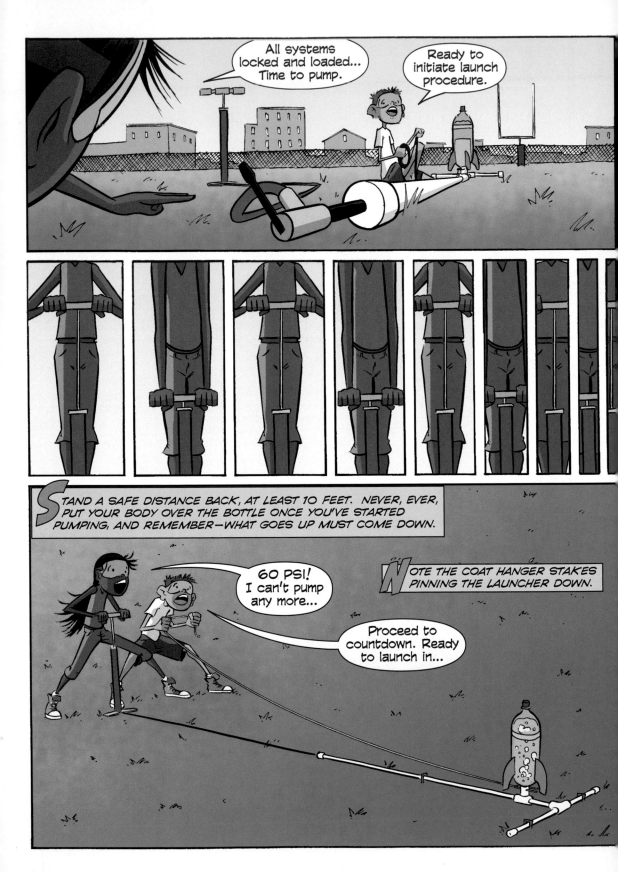

CELINE

- ANALYTICAL
- THOUGHTFUL

HEADS
- CIRCLE
- OVAL
CARVE CHINS

PEAR SHAPED
- BODY

SOLID SHAPE FOR HAIR!!

Dr. Saul Griffith is known as an inventor, but was trained as an engineer. He received his PhD at MIT. Since then Saul has used his training and skills to start numerous technology companies and has consistently championed STEAM education (including the A for ART!). Saul is currently running Otherlab, an independent research lab in San Francisco working on renewable energy, robotics, and advanced manufacturing technologies. Saul has been awarded numerous awards for invention including being named a MacArthur Fellow in 2007. Saul has dozens of patents in fields from aerospace to nanotechnology and enjoys being broadly trained as well as narrowly focused.

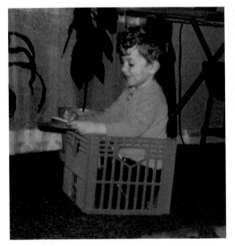

Nick Dragotta began his career at Marvel Comics working on titles as varied as X-Statix, The Age Of The Sentry, X-Men: First Class, Captain America: Forever Allies, Vengance, Fantastic Four #588, and FF. In addition, Nick is the co-creator and artist of the New York Times bestselling and Eisner nominated comic series East of West, with Jonathan Hickman at Image. He also works with Otherlab visualizing concepts.

Ingrid Dragotta is the designer and project manager for Howtoons. She also works as a designer for Otherlab. She earned her BFA in Product Design from the Savannah College of Art and Design and a DMBA in Design Strategy at California College of the Arts. Before Howtoons, Ingrid worked in the children's apparel and toy industries at New Balance Athletic Shoe Inc. and Hasbro, Inc.